MATHEMATWIST

NUMBER TALES FROM AROUND THE WORLD

t.v. padma

illustrated by **PROITI ROY**

Tulika

from the author

As a child, I loved the world of language as much as I loved the world of mathematics. When I went to college, I was forced to prioritise. I chose the latter, and it is a choice I have never regretted. Happily, in this book — the result of one of my dearest projects — I have been able to combine both!

The stories in this collection can be enjoyed by anyone at any age. But for those who wish to have a more precise idea of the 'level' of mathematical concepts I touch on, the topics covered are generally introduced during Classes 6, 7, and 8 in India; the Key Stage Two level in the United Kingdom; and the middle-grade age group in the United States.

As with any project, I was lucky to have the help of numerous friends and colleagues and would like to thank them: first and foremost, my spouse, Rainer Lohmann, for his steadfast support of all my writing endeavours; my mother, Ambujam Venkatraman, for her unwavering faith in me and in anything I decide to do; my 'mathematician' friends, Wan Fokkink and Nitu Kitchloo, for their generous offers to look over the mathematics in this book; my cousin Meena Sridhar, for spending so much time and energy looking over the mathematical concepts with her expert eye; Shobana Suresh, Ahalya Ananth, Prabha Rao, Siva Sundaresan and Marakatham Venkatraman, who assisted in different ways at different times; my friend Anita Shet, for her sincere enthusiasm; Katrice Lippa and Yared, for providing authentic Ethiopian names; Paul, Sylvia, Sharon, Roberta, and all the other helpful librarians at North Kingstown, Jamestown, and the University of Rhode Island; Deeya, Radhika, Sandhya, and all the others at

Tulika, for their hard work; Nannu chithappa, Bhanumurthy maama, Malati akka, Shuba akka, and Chinna akka, who encouraged my early interest in writing and mathematics; and last but not least, the children with whom I shared my love of science and mathematics, when I was the director and head of Inwoods, a school in the United Kingdom.

I would also like to acknowledge the Highlights Foundation and Carus publications, respectively, for allowing the re-use of *Sharing Parathas* (which first appeared in the magazine *Highlights for Children*) and *Rounding up Camels* (which first appeared in *Odyssey* magazine). My sincerest thanks to Christine French Clark, editor-in-chief of Highlights, and Lou Waryncia, editor-in-chief of Carus publications, for granting permission.

Two meticulously researched works on the non-European roots of science and mathematics were the starting point for my own research on the subject: *Lost Discoveries* by Dick Teresi and *The Crest of the Peacock* by George Gheverghese Joseph. Carol Vorderman's *How Maths Works* was another source of inspiration. I owe a great debt to these and other talented writers who popularise science and maths, and delve into the history of these subjects.

If you would like to read more about my previous work, please visit my website (www.cliofindia.com/padma), my webpage (www.padmasbooks.com), or my blog (http://padmasbooks.blogspot.com).

This book is dedicated to Siddhanth Sridhar, Roshan and Rishi Shet, Arjun Dhruve, Megha Krishnamurthi, Meera Krishnamoorthy, Aditya Venkatraman, Arathi Ramachandran, Ashwin Khamambhatty, Arul Venkatesh and Kalyan Fernandes, in the hope that they will always love books and mathematics.

CONTENTS

 The Eighth Donkey
a counting story from Armenia
page 6

 **Shortening a Line**
a play from India
page 13

 Double Trouble
a weighty Roman tale
page 20

 **Magic Squares**
a dramatised Chinese story
page 27

 **Powerful Moves**
a brainteaser from India
page 33

 **Dividing a Goose**
a Jewish story
page 42

Rounding up Camels
a folktale from India
page 48

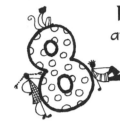

Filling a Space
an Ethiopian folktale
page 55

The Weight of a Crown
a legend from Greece
page 62

How Many Stars?
a folktale from India
page 67

Gourmet Roulette
a Russian brainteaser
page 72

A Fair Division
an Indian story
page 79

Criss-Cross Logic
a 'thinking' American story
page 86

Sixty-Four Rings to Heaven
a number tale from Vietnam
page 90

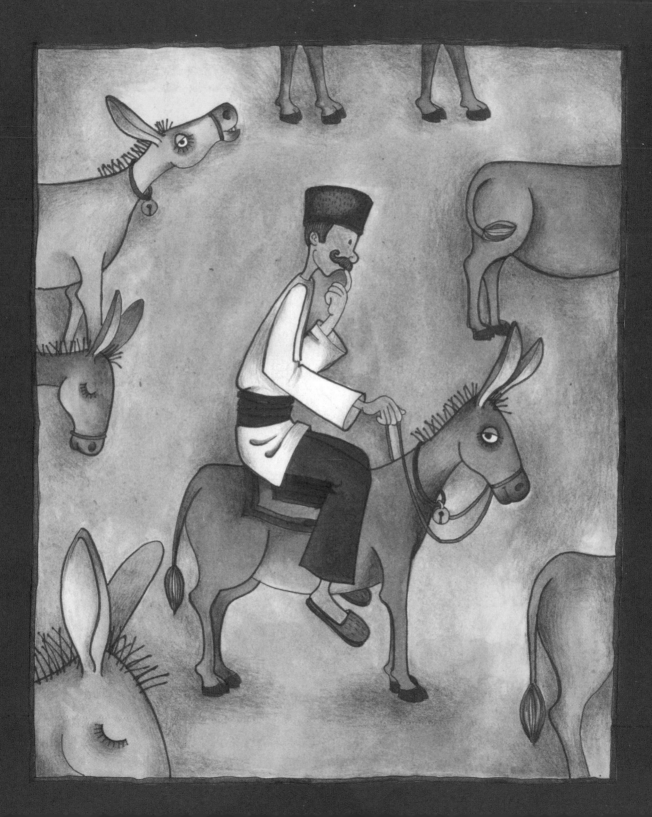

The Eighth Donkey

A counting story from Armenia

An Armenian merchant decided to sell some of his donkeys. Before he left the house, his wife said to him: "Make sure you count the donkeys often. Tie them tightly together and sell all seven. Don't lose any on the way."

The merchant nodded. He counted seven donkeys, mounted one of them and set off.

It was a long way to the market. When he had travelled a quarter of the distance, he counted his donkeys again just to be sure they were all still there.

"One, two, three, four, five, six," he counted. But where was the seventh? He could not see it in front of him. He could not see it behind him.

"I've lost one," he worried, and got off just to make sure he had roped them properly together. He checked all the knots. They seemed tight enough. Perhaps he had miscounted.

"One, two, three, four, five, six, seven," he counted again. There they all were! Delighted, he mounted one and continued his journey.

It was a long way to the market. When he reached the halfway mark, he counted his donkeys again just to be sure they were all still there.

"One, two, three, four, five, six," he counted. But where was the seventh?

He could not see it in front of him. He could not see it behind him.

"My wife will be so upset," he worried. How could one have slipped away?

Dismayed, the merchant climbed down and counted his donkeys again.

"One, two, three, four, five, six, seven. Ah, they are all here," he said with relief. He climbed on a donkey and continued towards the market.

When he was three-quarters of the way there, he decided to check on them once more.

"One, two, three, four, five, six," he counted.

"What?" he cried. "Again!"

It was nowhere in front. It was nowhere behind. How could it have disappeared?

"I must have missed something," he thought. He stopped at a nearby inn, tied up the donkeys and went in to have a long drink of water.

"Are those your seven donkeys?" asked the innkeeper, looking out of the window.

"Yes indeed," said the merchant excitedly. "Do you see seven?"

The innkeeper looked closely.

"Why, yes, I do," he said.

"Are you sure?"

"Of course I am," said the innkeeper, a little bewildered.

The merchant ran out joyfully and counted his donkeys again. Yes, there were seven.

"I do still have seven donkeys, I see," he said to himself. "What a great mystery this all is!"

The merchant continued almost all the way to the market. Just before he reached it, he checked on his donkeys one last time. The elusive seventh donkey was gone again!

"Where did it go?" he worried.

He tried to calm himself. "When I am on the ground, I seem to always have seven donkeys," he thought. "Perhaps I should get down and count them again, to see if I still have the seventh donkey."

So he dismounted and counted his donkeys and, sure enough, the seventh reappeared.

By now the merchant was very worried.

"These are expensive donkeys," he thought. "I am almost at the marketplace. Just to make sure I don't lose that seventh donkey, I'd better just walk the rest of the way."

So he walked beside his donkeys on the road to the market.

A little ahead, he saw a smart young lady walking beside her father.

"We have no animals to ride," she said to him, "so we are walking to the marketplace. But why are you walking instead of riding one of your donkeys?"

The merchant explained, looking very pleased with himself: "I have discovered something very interesting on this journey. I started with seven donkeys, but the moment I mount one of them, I find I only have six. When I get down, I find I have seven. I would rather have seven donkeys to sell than six, and so I decided it would be safest to walk to the marketplace, to make sure I don't lose my seventh donkey."

The woman looked very amused.

"Just seven?" she asked, "Why, my good man, I see no less than eight donkeys before me."

"Eight?" asked the merchant wonderingly.

"Yes," she smiled. "According to my count, there are eight donkeys going to the marketplace."

The woman seemed so smart that the merchant did not bother to question her. When he reached the marketplace, he shouted loudly,

"Eight donkeys for sale! Eight donkeys for sale!"

A rich man came by and looked at the merchant's donkeys.

"Eight?" he said, with surprise. "I only see seven."

"It is a great mystery," the merchant said. "I started the day with seven donkeys, but on the way I met a smart young woman who said she saw a total of eight donkeys on the way to the marketplace."

The man laughed and they counted together, and the merchant found he only had the seven he had started with. The man paid for the donkeys and left.

On the way back, the merchant wondered for a while about what had happened, but in the end he was satisfied that he had done at least what he had set out to do. He had made a good profit.

"That poor woman was not as clever as she looked," he thought. "She must never have learned to count."

And all the way home, he thought with great pity about the poor woman who did not know how to count correctly.

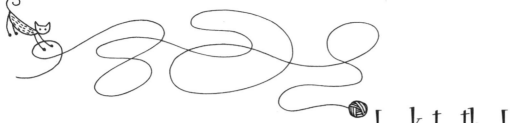

Mathematics began with a need to count, and then to record what was counted. All across the globe, ancient cultures discovered unique and interesting ways of counting.

In a place called Ishango, between Uganda and Zaire at the centre of Africa, archaeologists have unearthed the remains of people who lived during the New Stone Age. One of the most interesting finds was an old bone that was apparently a tool of some sort. This is engraved with groups of lines that are too asymmetrical to be decorative. Some mathematicians and archaeologists think that this bone shows how the people of Ishango had a well-developed sense of arithmetic. The bone might have been a way for them to record the passage of seasons, like a calendar.

The Incas of South America had a highly sophisticated system of counting called quipu, which meant knot. A quipu is a set of strings or cords, usually dyed in different colours. The strings contain many different types of knots. When the Inca Empire reached its zenith around the 15th century CE, it was vast, covering parts of present-day Peru, Bolivia, Chile, Ecuador and Argentina. It is believed that the Incas preserved important numerical records about their kingdom using quipus — for example, information on their population of around 6,000,000 in different provinces of the empire.

In Central America, the Mayan empire of the early 16th century extended across parts of modern Belize, Guatemala, El Salvador, and the Honduras. They invented a number system in which numbers were written

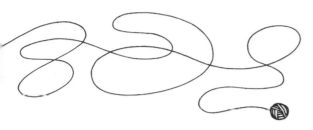

using dots and lines. One of the most interesting aspects of this system was that the Mayans independently invented the zero. The Mayans even invented a symbol for zero! The ancient Babylonians and the Indians are also said to have independently invented the zero. Strange, isn't it, that ancient people across the globe made similar discoveries all on their own?

Shortening a line

A play from India

Cast of characters:
Narrator
Akbar, the Mughal Emperor
Birbal, the wise minister
Four courtiers

Scene: A garden. Towards the front of the stage is a patch of freshly-dug soil. At the back, Emperor Akbar and Birbal are walking, deep in conversation. The courtiers are standing at the front the stage.

Narrator   Once upon a time, there lived in India a Mughal emperor called Akbar. The wisest man in his court was Birbal, who was therefore a great favourite with the Emperor. This made the other courtiers jealous — they would naturally be happier if Akbar liked them instead. So, every now and again, they hatched plans to make Birbal look foolish in front of the Emperor. One day, King Akbar and Birbal were walking along in the garden, followed by the usual retinue of disgruntled courtiers . . .

Courtier 1   Look at them, always together.

Courtier 2   The Emperor has no time for anyone but Birbal. He is so impressed with him!

Courtier 3   But Birbal is wise. And so witty! He makes Huzoor laugh.

Courtier 4   Yes, he also solves any problem that comes up before the Emperor.

Courtier 2   Hah! We shall soon see how smart he is. Listen, I have an idea . . .

They huddle together in one corner of the stage, whispering. Akbar and Birbal sit down. Courtier 1 then walks up to Akbar, and bows deeply.

Courtier 1   Huzoor, we have just been discussing a simple test of wisdom. We thought it might interest you.

Akbar   *(laughing)* What is this test, my good man?

Courtier 2   One that everyone fails, Huzoor.

Akbar: Rubbish! There is one man in my court who can do the impossible. He does it every time. You know as well as I, who that person is.

Courtier 3   You mean Birbal, Huzoor?

Akbar   Naturally.

Courtier 4   I beg your pardon, Emperor, but this is a problem that not even he can solve.

Akbar   Hmmm! Did you hear that, Birbal? Are you ready for a challenge?

Birbal   *(bows)* It will be my pleasure to try, Huzoor.

The courtiers gather around Akbar and Birbal.

Courtier 2   *(to Birbal)* Draw a line in the mud.

Akbar   Here, take my royal staff, Birbal. Draw the line with it.

Akbar hands Birbal a staff. Birbal bows to Akbar, then uses the staff to draw a nice, long line in the patch of soil.

Courtier 1   Now, without touching the line, shorten it.

Birbal   You mean I must somehow make this line shorter without erasing any part of it?

Courtier 4   That is precisely what we mean! Make the line shorter without tampering with it in any way at all. *(Aside to Courtier 2)* Now watch the great Birbal fall!

Birbal looks at the line thoughtfully. He walks around it, then crouches beside it. The courtiers look at one another gleefully.

Akbar   Come on, Birbal! Surely this is not too great a challenge for you?

Birbal   Just a little more time, Huzoor.

Narrator   It seemed as if the courtiers would succeed this time . . . This was a tough one, even for Birbal. Make a line shorter without touching it? Is it possible?

Birbal   *(to Akbar)* It can be done, Emperor. *(He smiles and stands up.)*

Akbar   *(delighted)* It can?

The courtiers look surprised and dismayed.

Birbal   May I borrow your staff again, Huzoor?

Akbar   Of course!

Birbal takes it and draws a line next to the old one, much longer than the first.

Birbal   *(giving back the staff)* The first line is now shorter, Huzoor.

The courtiers look at the two lines, stunned.

Courtier 4 But . . . but . . . that is another line . . .

Birbal Yes it is. It makes the first look shorter, doesn't it? Isn't that what you wanted?

Akbar *(clapping)* Oh, wonderful! I knew it, dear Birbal! I knew you would find a way. I was a little worried this time . . . but you think so differently. It is a pleasure to follow your mind!

Akbar spontaneously takes off one of his jewelled necklaces and gives it to Birbal, along with a warm hug. They walk away, leaving the disconsolate courtiers behind.

Narrator And so, another attempt failed! It made Birbal look smarter than ever, and he remained Akbar's wisest and most loved minister until the end of his days.

siZe wise...

Birbal's famous wisdom partly stemmed from the fact that he thought 'differently', as the Emperor pointed out — out of the box, we may say. He was quick to realise that 'shorten' implied comparative size, and so switched to that train of thought.

Comparison — ordering numbers and comparing their sizes — is an important mathematical concept, with special signs. Mathematicians invented a quick way to write 'greater than' and 'less than'. The sign for greater than is $>$ and the sign for less than is $<$ and so we can write $2 < 20$ (instead of writing the words two is less than twenty) or, we can also write $20 > 2$ (which is a mathematical way to write that twenty is greater than two.

Indo-Arabic numbers are made of one or more of these 'digits': 0, 1, 2, 3, 4, 5, 6, 7, 8, and 9. It is easy to order numbers in terms of size, if all numbers in a list have the same number of digits, and they are all positive (greater than 0, such as 1, 2, 10, 11, 122, 156, etc). For example, if you need to order the 3-digit numbers 120, 241, 259, this is what you need to do. Look at the number with the smallest first digit. That's the lowest. In this case, 120 is the smallest number, because its first digit is 1 and the other two numbers have 2 as their first digits.

What should you do about the other two numbers, both of which have 2 as a first digit? Look to the right, and the number with the smaller second digit is less than the number with the larger second digit. So 120 is the smallest and 259 is the biggest number in this list. Now, you can write $120 < 241 < 259$ (or 120 is less than 241, which is less than 259).

When you arrange numbers from smallest to largest, it is called 'ascending' order. You could, of course, also arrange them the opposite way, which would be from largest to smallest. This is called 'descending' order. Descending order would be 259 > 241 > 120 (or 259 is greater than 241, which is greater than 120).

What if numbers don't have the same number of digits? Then, assuming all the numbers are positive (greater than zero) and whole (don't have a fractional or decimal part), then here's what you can do. Group numbers based on the number of digits they have. The ones with the fewest digits should be lower than those with more digits.

For example, if you have 69, 320, 14, 55 and 3567, first group the numbers. Numbers 69, 14 and 55 are 2-digit numbers, so they are shorter and smaller than the 3-digit numbers. Within this group of 2-digit numbers, you should use the rule we mentioned above, and arrange them. In ascending order, you could write, 14, 55, 69, or 14 < 55 < 69. What next? The 3-digit number 320 is shorter and smaller than the 4-digit number 3567. All positive 3-digit whole numbers are lower than all positive 4-digit whole numbers. So, 320 < 3567. Putting the whole series in ascending order, you could write: 14, 55, 69, 320, 3567; or 14 < 55 < 69 < 320 < 3567. Or, equally well, you could write in descending order: 3567, 320, 69, 55, 14; or 3567 > 320 > 69 > 55 > 14. Remember, this works only with positive numbers, not negative numbers!

Double Trouble

A weighty Roman tale

The Roman general Terentius was returning after a victorious campaign.

The crowds cheered as he mounted the stairs to the Senate chamber, his helmet flashing proudly in the sunlight.

"Ave, Caesar!" Terentius saluted.

"Ave, Terentius!" Caesar replied. "As a reward for your services to Rome, you shall have a place in the Senate."

Terentius bowed his thanks, but remained silent because he thought he deserved more than just the honour of being part of the Senate.

"Is there anything else that you wish to have?" asked Caesar.

"O generous Caesar," said Terentius. "It is a great reward to have a position in the respected Senate. But I should also like to live out the rest of my days in prosperity. Is there not enough in the treasury to give me the small sum of a million denarii?"

"A million?" Caesar was shocked. That would drain the treasury! But the crowd was roaring its approval of the general's request and Caesar had to think quickly.

"Brave Terentius," he declared. "A great warrior must receive a suitably great reward. Let me suggest something that is worthy of your strength and remind us constantly of it. Instead of giving you our usual brass coins, allow us to make special coins just for you.

"Today, you may take one brass coin out of our treasury but, starting tomorrow, we shall mint coins to commemorate your campaign. Tomorrow, you shall have a coin weighing twice as much as the first, with twice the value of the first. The day after tomorrow, we shall make you a coin weighing twice as much as the second, with twice the value of the second. On the fourth day after your return, we shall ensure that a coin is minted with two times the value and weight of the third coin.

"On each day, a coin shall await you with a value and weight twice that of the previous day. You shall carry the coins out yourself, and the people of Rome shall cheer you on."

The crowd was delighted to think of the entertaining reward that Caesar had suggested. They shouted with excitement.

"I thank you for your generosity, O Caesar!" Terentius cried, his eyes glinting as he thought of all the money he would carry away. "It is indeed a just reward."

"Come, let us get your first coin," Caesar said, and led Terentius to the treasury. Terentius grabbed a handful of coins.

"Just one today," Caesar reminded him.

Caesar had the coin weighed. It was about 5 grams. He gave orders that a 10-gram coin with twice the value of the first be minted for Terentius to take the next day.

Terentius carried it away easily the following day, as he did his third, which weighed 20 grams, and had the value of four brass coins. The fourth, which weighed 40 grams, was valued at eight brass coins; the fifth, which weighed 80 grams, amounted to 16 brass coins; the sixth, which weighed 160 grams, was equal to 32 brass coins.

Terentius was a strong man. The crowds watched with pride as he carried coin after coin high above his head each day.

On the seventh day, Caesar had a coin minted that weighed 320 grams, and was equal to 64 brass coins. On the eighth day, Caesar greeted the general graciously as he carried away his special coin, weighing 640 grams, with the value of 128 brass coins.

The ninth day dawned and there was a coin weighing 1.28 kilograms, worth 256 brass coins; on the tenth, a coin weighing 2.56 kilograms, worth 512 brass coins; on the eleventh, a coin weighing 5.12 kilograms, worth 1,024 brass coins.

The crowd noticed that the general was no longer carrying the coins high above his head.

On the twelfth day, as the general carried away a coin weighing 10.24 kilograms and worth 2,048 brass coins, Caesar stopped by solicitously to ask Terentius if all this carrying was tiring him.

Terentius threw back his head and laughed. "It will take a long time before I tire, noble Caesar," he said.

On the thirteenth day, Terentius's coin weighed 20.48 kilograms, and amounted to 4,096 brass coins. The crowd noticed a bead of perspiration under the general's helmet as he carried his coin away in the heat of the noonday sun.

On the fourteenth day, Terentius was frowning, not smiling, under the weight of his 40.96-kilogram coin. He reminded himself that it was worth a lot of money: 8,192 brass coins.

On the fifteenth day, Caesar smiled warmly at Terentius. "Today's coin weighs nearly 82 kilos," he announced. "Surely that is no more than the weight of a strong warrior?"

"I have carried many men upon my shoulders!" Terentius replied, and onto his broad back he propped the coin that was worth 16,384 brass coins. He walked away, heaving with the strain of his burden.

The general's legs were shaking on the sixteenth day, sweat pouring in a steady stream from under his helmet as he carried a coin weighing 163.84 kilograms.

"32,768," he muttered to himself under his breath, puffing as he walked along the path the crowd had created for him.

On the seventeenth day, Terentius rolled his unwieldy, 327.68-kilogram coin — worth 65, 536 brass coins — along the ground.

On the eighteenth day, Terentius had to use his spear as a steering lever, to prod and push his 655.360 kg coin, worth 131,072 brass coins.

"No pickpocket could ever steal that coin," Caesar pointed out.

"Enough, Caesar, enough!" Terentius gasped. "This is my last visit to the treasury. I wish for no more."

Caesar smiled. Terentius had asked for 1,000,000 denarii or 5,000,000 brass coins. Instead he got money worth less than 300,000 brass coins.

Caesar had saved the city of Rome a lot of money.

The Romans didn't have kilograms as a weight measure, although it has been used in the story for the sake of simplicity. They even wrote numbers differently; a very fancy way still used, for example, with names of kings and queens. Queen Elizabeth III looks much grander than Queen Elizabeth the 3rd, doesn't it?

Romans wrote the numbers 1 to 10 using these symbols: I, II, III, IV, V, VI, VII, VIII, IX, X. Fifty had a special symbol, which was L; one hundred was C; and a thousand was M. Some Roman numbers were made up by adding — such as VI (Roman for 6), which is really V plus I, or 5+1. VII (Roman for 7) has V followed by two 'I's, which means 5+1+1 and equals 7. Some numbers were based on subtraction: such as IX (Roman for 9), which means X minus I or 10 – 1.

Roman numerals aren't used very often, though. That's because they are not as consistent as the numerals we use more commonly (0,1,2,3,4,5,6,7,8, and 9). This Indo-Arabic system, the most widely used numeral system in the world today, was invented in India centuries ago and is believed to have travelled westward with Arab traders.

Why did this system become so popular? Indo-Arabic numerals are based on a place value system — meaning that the placement of numbers to each other is important. These numbers are also easy to recognise and progress using a consistent logic, giving us a lot of clear information. For instance, when we write the number 10, it means that the number contains one 'ten' and no 'units'. When we write 123, we are communicating that the number is composed of one 'hundred', two 'tens', and three 'units'. In other words (or numbers!), 123 = [(1x100) + (2x10) + (3x1)]. A few other ancient writing systems, like the ancient Chinese number system, also had a place value system.

The Indo-Arabic system allowed human beings to dream up higher mathematics by making the world of arithmetic easier and more accessible. Even slightly complicated arithmetic becomes harder with most other forms of number writing. Take a look at this problem:
19×100 = ? Easy, isn't it? In Indo-Arabic numbers, yes. 19×100 = 1900. But written the Roman way, the same calculation would look like: XIX×C. The answer 1900 would be written as MCM [1000 + (1000−100)] — grander to look at, but inconvenient to use.

Magic Squares

A dramatised Chinese story

Cast of characters
Narrator
Emperor Yu
Four courtiers

Scene: The Emperor and his courtiers are standing in a boat against a backdrop of water. Towards the front of the stage, supposedly on the bank, is a large cardboard turtle.

Narrator   Four thousand and a few hundred years ago, a great Emperor called Yu ruled over China. The Emperor had sharp eyes and an even sharper mind. One lovely day, the Emperor and his courtiers were drifting down the River Lo in a beautiful boat . . .

Emperor   *(pointing to the bank)* Look! Look!

Courtier 1   What do you see, Your Royal Highness?

Emperor   Look at that turtle climbing on the bank! Stop the boat. I want to get off.

The Emperor and his courtiers climb off the boat.

Emperor   Bring me that turtle.

A courtier picks up the cardboard turtle. He holds it up to show the audience and then hands it to the Emperor.

Emperor   Amazing! A wonder of nature!

Courtier 2   Your Highness? Oh yes, lovely colours.

Courtier 3   What a sturdy shell!

Courtier 1   No, no, His Majesty is talking about its size.

Narrator   No, no. The Emperor knows his mathematics . . .

Emperor   Not colour and size. The squares on the turtle's back — aren't they fascinating?

Narrator   But not, unfortunately, his courtiers . . .

The three courtiers scratch their heads and look puzzled.

Narrator   Except this one . . .

Courtier 4   There are three squares across and three squares down. This is a grid, Your Highness.

Emperor   Yes! And within the grid are dots. A message! A remarkable mathematical message, written on the turtle's back!

The Emperor holds up the turtle to show the audience and then hands it to one of the courtiers.

Narrator   The poor courtiers looked all over the turtle but . . .

Courtiers   *(together)* Message?

Emperor   Count the dots!

Narrator   Ah! *That* they know how to do . . .

Courtier 3   *(counting)* This row has one square with eight dots, one with one dot and the last square has six dots.

Courtier 1   The middle row has three, five and seven dots on the squares.

Courtier 2   And the bottom row has four, nine and two. And so . . .? *(He turns desperately to Courtier 4 for help.)*

Courtier 4   These are magic squares on the turtle's back, Your Most Glorious and Intelligent Highness!

The Emperor smiles and nods. The other three whisper among themselves agitatedly.

Emperor   The sum of the dots in the first row is fifteen, the sum of the dots in the second row is fifteen, and so is the sum of dots in the third row.

Courtier 4   And have you counted the sums of dots in each column, Your Highness?

The Emperor stares at the turtle, which is still being held up by one of the courtiers.

Emperor   The totals of all the columns are the same. This is incredible!

Courtier 4   So are the sums of the diagonals. All add up to fifteen.

Emperor   Carry the turtle carefully back to the palace. This is a treasure. I would like it to be well cared for as long as it lives.

Narrator   The turtle lived for long, long time, as turtles do; even longer than the Emperor, in fact. It roamed peacefully in the palace gardens. Visitors came from all over the world to gaze in amazement at the magic square pattern on its back, which was later named the Lo-shu.

number fun ...

A magic square is a square grid of numbers, in which each row and each column adds up to the same sum. So if you add numbers along the diagonals, or in a straight horizontal or vertical line, you'll end up with the same answer.

One way to create or solve magic squares is by trial and error. Of course, that takes a long time, especially if your square is larger than the 3 by 3 grid in the story. Imagine a 4 by 4 magic square   that is already a lot more work than a 3 by 3 square.

If you look carefully at the magic squares given for you to work out, you'll find that there are symmetries in the ways that numbers are arranged within them. Using these symmetries, many mathematically intelligent people formulated methods for creating magic squares. Some famous names who were fascinated by magic squares: Benjamin Franklin from the USA; the German artist Albrecht Duerer; Emanuel Moschopoulus, who lived in Istanbul in the 1300s; Narayana Pandit of India, who lived in the mid-1300s; Philippe de la Hire of France, who lived between 1640 and 1719; and the Swiss mathematician Leonhard Euler, who lived between 1707 and 1783.

Some mathematicians extend the idea of magic squares to describe any kind of grid that shows an interesting and predictable pattern among the numbers within the grid. Sudoku are ancient Japanese number puzzles that have had a recent revival in modern times — showing that the people of today can be just as fascinated by the magic of numbers as people were in olden times.

Some cultures felt that magic squares had a religious significance. In Spain, magic squares were sometimes carved into the walls of cathedrals.

Arab mathematicians of long ago found magic squares as pleasing as the ancient Chinese. They liked creating and solving complicated magic squares, and called this activity the 'science of secrets'.

Like the Chinese, the ancient Arabs made numerous fundamental contributions to mathematics. The word 'algebra' has an Arabic root.

Here's a magic square for you to try. Some of the numbers are filled in, to give you a place to start. Can you complete it correctly?

5		
	4	
1		3

Powerful Moves

A brainteaser from India

There lived in ancient India a sage called Sissa. He was a scholarly, gentle man, and an innovative teacher. One of Sissa's great inventions was the game of chess, played on a chequered board, with sixty-four alternating white and black squares. He hoped this would help his students learn to plan ahead and to concentrate. It did, and they were fascinated.

Soon, everyone in the kingdom was playing chess. Sheram, too, the king of the realm. One morning, as he moved one of the gilded pieces on his marble chessboard, a question entered his mind.

"Who invented this remarkable game?" he asked.

"One of your own subjects, sire," replied a courtier. "A wise man by the name of Sissa."

"I must reward this man. Bring him here — in comfort, and escorted," he commanded grandly.

At once, a retinue of soldiers and courtiers sped off to Sissa's village. Sissa agreed to the king's request and the very next morning he entered the king's chess chamber, dressed as always in well-worn clothes.

"You invented this game?" the king asked in surprise. Having hardly ever stepped out of his palace, he had never seen someone who was so simply dressed.

Sissa smiled and nodded.

The king looked the sage up and down again. "You do not look wealthy, although you look well for a man of your years. Ask for anything you desire and it will be yours. I am wealthier than even a man of your imagination could possibly conceive, and I shall ensure that you are soon as rich as you deserve to be," he said generously.

Sissa was a man who always thought before he spoke, and so he did not say what first entered his mind, that he was truly content and had no wish at all. But then it came to him that he did have a wish after all.

His silence troubled the king.

"Do not hesitate," he said. "Speak your mind." He waved his bejewelled fingers in a lavish gesture. "Look at this chessboard — it is made of marble and precious metals. Look at me — I am dressed in the finest silks. Everywhere around you is wealth. You have to only tell me what you desire and I shall give it to you."

"Generous King," said Sissa, "I am a simple sage and my needs too are simple. I ask only for this: some grain from your granary."

"Grain?" said the King in surprise. "Surely you want something else? Gold? Silver? Precious gems? Silks to wear and soft carpets to walk on? Servants to wait upon you? A palace of your own?"

"Grains of wheat are all that I want," replied Sissa gently. "As it is the power of my chessboard that brought me here, I ask that you give me grains of wheat in exchange for the squares on your chessboard. For the first square, I would like two grains of wheat. For the second, I would like two multiplied by itself, which is four grains of wheat. On the third square, the number of grains should be two raised to the power of three, which is two multiplied by itself three times, which is eight grains of wheat. So, following that pattern, I would like sixteen grains of wheat on the fourth square. And so on, until the sixty-fourth square."

"Is that all? Are you sure?"

"I am certain," said Sissa. "The grains of wheat you give me will follow the sequence 2, 4, 8, 16, and so on, and I like that sequence of numbers."

"If this is what you wish, consider it given," said the king. "I took you for a wise man, but now I wonder! Take your sack of grain and you may return to your village."

"I am an old man, sire," said Sissa. "Even a small sack of grain would be too heavy for me to carry. May I ask that you send this grain to my village?"

"Of course," said the King. "Your grain will reach you by sunset."

Sissa smiled and left.

The king spent the rest of the day busy with the affairs of his kingdom, leaving the prime minister to see to Sissa's reward. When the sun had almost set, the king realised that the prime minister had still not returned from the granary, and summoned him.

The prime minister walked up to the throne a few minutes later and stood looking at the floor, twisting his robes with his hands.

"Has that foolish sage's sack of grain been sent to him yet?" the king asked.

The prime minister shook his head slowly, still refusing to meet the king's eye.

"Why?" asked the King, exasperated.

"We are still counting the grains, your Highness."

"Still counting the grains?" thundered the king, getting angrier every minute. "What do you mean, still counting the grains? I promised to send him his sack by sunset and thanks to your tardiness I will, for the first time in my life, be forced to break my word!"

"It is not my tardiness, sire, I assure you," said the prime minister, raising his eyes at last. "It is the sage's cleverness that may force you to reconsider your decision."

"Reconsider?" said the King. "I never reconsider! Get the royal accountant or someone who is good at counting to help you and make sure the reward is dispensed by sunset tomorrow, at the very latest."

"I will do my best, sire," said the prime minister.

The next evening, as the sun was setting in the sky, the king asked for the prime minister to be brought before him again.

Instead, the royal astronomer appeared before the court. He was known for his skill with numbers and calculation.

"Your Highness, I request your permission to speak in the prime minister's stead," he said.

"What is that blundering fool doing, taking so long over dispensing a simple reward?" yelled the king.

The astronomer faced the king calmly. "Why don't we sit down together and talk it over," he suggested.

The king was not used to being overruled, but he was so angry and upset that he could not think of anything to say.

The astronomer continued quickly, "You do not have enough grain in your granary to cover the sage's request. Indeed, there isn't enough money in your treasury to buy the amount of grain that you have promised to give him."

"That's impossible!" hissed the king. "Impossible!"

"Let me show you why," said the astronomer. With a flourish, he wrote down the numbers from 1 to 64 in a long column on the left of a scroll. "Let's see," he said, enjoying the king's discomfiture. "For the first square on the chessboard, we owe Sissa just 2 grains of wheat. The number 2 can be expressed as 2 raised to the power of 1. Any number raised to the power of 1 is, in fact, itself. That's a rule, really, a definition, so just accept my word for it."

"Fine. Fine," said the king, still rattled

"For the second square on the chessboard, we owe Sissa 2 raised to the power of 2, or 2 multiplied by itself, or 2x2, which is 4 grains of wheat."

"So?" said the king.

"So, the sequence continues. For the third square, we owe Sissa 8 grains of wheat, or the number 2 raised to the third power, or 2 cubed, if you follow . . . ?"

"I know what 2 cubed is," said the king. "Cubing is multiplying a number by itself three times, in this case, it's 2x2x2, which is equal to 8."

"Quite," said the royal astronomer agreeably. "For the fourth square, we owe him the number 2 raised to the power of 4. That, as I am sure your highness is well aware, is nothing but 2x2x2x2, which equals 16."

"So what?" said the king. "We have to add up all the wheat grains we get from the sequence of 2 raised to powers in increments of 1, starting with the number 2 itself. So we start with 2^1, 2^2, 2^3, 2^4, and so on, until we get to 2^{64}, which is what we'd owe him for the final square. How long does that take?"

"Your Highness," said the royal astronomer. "I've no doubt that you will be able to work it out on your own. Why don't you tell us what the final figure is?"

"Sure!" said the King. "I can do it in my head."

He sat still for a few minutes, absorbed in calculation.

"Give me that scroll, would you please?" he said after a while, reaching for it with a flourish. "I am losing track of it in my head, with all those twos, but it will be easier on paper."

The royal astronomer handed him the scroll and slipped away quietly. That night, the king did not return to his chambers. He was working out the problem.

As the sun rose the next morning, the king rose from his throne at last, looking very weary. "Send the prime minister to me," he said quietly.

The prime minister walked in, looking like a man who had not slept in a while.

"I spent the night working it out myself," said King Sheram. "I know now why you were unable to fulfill my foolish promise to the wise sage. For the sixty-fourth square alone, we owe him about 18, 446,744,073,709,600,000 grains.

"I remember the royal architect telling me once that a cubic metre of wheat contains about 15,000,000 grains. I have been trying to imagine how large a granary could hold the amount of grain that Sissa requested. If we imagine a granary 4 times the height and 10 metres in width, with a length of 300,000,000 kilometres, would even that be enough, I have been asking myself. Would it?

For even such a large granary would only have a capacity of about 12,000 cubic kilometres, or 12,000,000,000,000 cubic metres."

The prime minister nodded wearily.

"If all the land on earth was sown with wheat, sire, it would still not yield the grain we have promised," he said softly.

King Sheram smiled.

"Yes, yes, I know," he said. "You deserve some sleep, my good man. But before that, make sure you request that Sissa be brought to court again."

The next day, when Sissa arrived, the king prostrated himself before the sage.

"You have humbled me," he said. "There is not enough grain in all the world to satisfy your request."

Sissa smiled. "I don't need your grain," he said. "But there are many in your kingdom who do. Giving brings more joy and contentment than wealth and riches."

The king bowed his head, and Sissa blessed him. Then Sissa departed on foot to return to his village, where he played a quiet game of chess with one of his students before going to bed.

Multiplication is one of the four fundamental arithmetical skills. The others are of course addition, subtraction and division. Arithmetic is that part of mathematics that is intimately involved with numbers. The word comes from the ancient Greek work 'arithmetike', which means art of numbers.

Squaring is a very special type of multiplication. Suppose you want to multiply the number two by itself (or twice). Then, you could write 2×2, or, you could also write 2^2 which would be read as 'two squared' or 'two raised to the power of two' which is, of course, the number 4.

Cubing means multiplying a number by itself, three times. So two cubed would mean the same as saying two raised to the power of three, which would be written mathematically as $2 \times 2 \times 2$, or 2^3, equal to 8.

There are no terms like 'squaring' and 'cubing' when numbers are raised to powers other than two and three. Why? Probably because they would be hard to visualise. You could think of the number two, for example, as a line which is 2 units long (2 cms, or 2 mm, or 2 km). So you can visualise two squared, or 2^2 as an actual square, in which each side is 2 units long (for example, a square which is 2 cm wide and 2 cm long).

Now, cubing. You can visualise 2^3 as a cube, in which each side is 2 units long (say, 2 cm high, 2 cm wide, and 2 cm long).

You can raise numbers to powers other than just 2 or 3. In the story, the number 2 was raised to different powers. But can you imagine what 2^4 would look like, following the logic of squares and cubes?

It's much harder, because we live in a world where there are 3 dimensions: length, breadth (or width) and height. The fourth dimension is

written about in science fiction, but it takes a lot of imagination to think of that. And beyond the fourth dimension? Exciting to think of . . . but very difficult to see even in the mind's eye.

In fact, that's part of the reason that the Greeks stopped with squares and cubes. Some other ancient cultures, including the Indians, understood that numbers could be raised to powers other than 2 or 3, even though it defied their visual imagination. This made it possible for ancient Indians to use what we now call 'logarithms'. Logarithms helped people to multiply and divide large numbers before the age of computers and pocket calculators. Although logarithms were in use in India, the western world wasn't aware of them until the seventeenth century. At that time, a man called John Napier independently invented logarithms.

What about raising numbers to powers below (rather than above) two and three? That's hard to visualise, too, but easier mathematically. What is 2^1? If you follow the logic, that is just 2; in fact, any number raised to the power of one is just the number itself.

What's 2^0? We define powers such that any number raised to the power of zero is equal to one. So 2^0 is the same as 64^0 or 108^0 . . . all of those are just equal to 1.

Many ancient people were fascinated with squaring numbers. In the region that is now the Middle East, Mesopotamian astronomers kept extensive tables of squares as long ago as 2000 BCE. Babylonians also kept multiplication tables, tables of squares, tables of cubes, and much, much more.

Dividing a Goose

A Jewish story

There was once a poor peasant who found himself at the table with his wife and children, but with nothing for them to eat.

"What shall we do?" he cried in despair. "We are out of food and in the thick of winter."

"You will think of a way to find us something to eat," his wife replied with confidence.

"We have nothing," said the peasant, "except that goose I see outside the window. It is not enough to feed all of us."

"Well, something is better than nothing," said his wife.

"Not enough," the peasant muttered. "One goose is not enough for us all."

His wife stood straight and tall, and looked him in the eye and said, "I am sure you will make it enough."

So the peasant stepped out into the snow and killed the goose. In the distance, he saw a carriage roll by — the carriage of the wealthy Barin of the village.

He had an idea.

"I will go to the Barin," he said, "and I will make this goose enough for all of us to eat well."

The peasant went to the Barin's home and said, "I have brought you this goose as a gift. It is all that I and my family have."

"Thank you," said the Barin. "We never disdain a gift. Now you must join us at our table for supper. But tell me, how do you think you can divide one goose among us?"

At the table with the Barin sat his wife, two sons and two daughters.

"I will divide this goose most fairly," the peasant said, picking up the carving knife. "You are the head of the house," he said to the Barin, "so the goose's head belongs to you and your wife."

The Barin smiled, pleased. "That is wise," he said.

The peasant cut off the two legs and handed one to each of the sons. "Soon you will leave home and walk new paths of your own," he said.

The boys sat up straighter, feeling important.

The peasant cut off the bird's wings, and handed them to the two daughters. "You will soar into the sky one day," he said to them. "Here are wings for you to fly with."

The daughters were charmed.

"And I'll take what's left of the goose, if you don't mind," the peasant said finally, to the Barin.

"Not at all," said the Barin. "But as you have done such a fine job of dividing the goose, shall I not give you a goose to take home to your family?"

The peasant, however, had other ideas.

"That would be too kind," he said. "Instead, let me help divide the five other geese that I see at your table among us all again, if I may."

"If that is your wish, why not!" said the Barin, "I would gladly see you make another fair division, though you are welcome to take home a whole bird."

The peasant took one of the five geese and presented it to the Barin and his wife.

"Now you are three," he said.

He took a second goose and gave it to the Barin's two sons.

"Now you are also three," he said.

The third goose he placed before the daughters.

"Now we too are three," they said happily.

"And these geese and I are three," said the peasant, drawing the two remaining geese towards himself.

So the peasant left for home with two more birds under his arm than the one he had started with – plus a reward of gold from the Barin for his remarkable ability to divide geese and resolve issues gracefully.

a walk to the past ...

An easy way to think of division is that it is a mathematical word for 'sharing'. If you wanted to share 10 sweets equally among 5 children, you could write, mathematically, $10 \div 5$.

Division and subtraction are related to one another in a way that's similar to the relationship between multiplication and addition. Division is really just repeated subtraction. So $10 \div 5$ is like saying, take 5 away from 10 as many times as you can. How many times can you do this? Twice. That's because if you take 5 away from 10 once, you'll be left with five; or, $10 - 5 = 5$. You can, of course, take another 5 away from this remainder, but after that you'll be left with zero so you'll have to stop $(5 - 5 = 0)$. So $10 \div 5 = 2$, because you can take 5 away from 10 two times.

Similarly, multiplication is just repeated addition. For instance, 2×3 is nothing more than adding 2 three times: $2 + 2 + 2$ (or, if you will, 3 lots of 2); you could equally well think of 2×3 as adding the number 3 two times: $3 + 3$ (or, 2 lots of 3). In multiplication (and addition), order doesn't matter. So $2 \times 3 = 3 \times 2$.

Symbols for arithmetic operations have existed for centuries. Of course, different cultures used different signs for adding, subtracting, dividing and multiplying. The ancient Egyptian symbols for addition and subtraction look a little like stick figures of men walking forwards or backwards!

In 1881, in northwest India, a farmer was digging the earth when he found a stone enclosure. Within it, were 70 pieces of birch bark. On the bark was

something written in ancient Sanskrit. He recognised that this was an incredibly important find. Though he protected it, preserved it and brought attention to it, much of it was destroyed when it was examined. Luckily, although its significance was suppressed by English scholars such as G. R. Kaye who attempted to translate it (and often lacked a thorough enough knowledge of ancient Sanskrit, or sought to attribute all major mathematical advances to the Greeks), its remains have been preserved at Oxford.

This document, called the Bakhshali manuscript, is probably the oldest Indian mathematical text that seems devoid of any religious connotation. It covers a variety of topics: fractions, square roots, arithmetic, profit, loss, interest, and far more advanced mathematics. There are symbols to denote negative numbers. Numbers that are multiplied are placed next to one another, and numbers that are divided are placed one on top of the other.

How old is the Bakhshali manuscript? Scholars disagree — some say it was written in the seventh century CE at the very latest, others place it at around 400 CE. Old enough, one way or another!

Rounding up Camels

A folktale from India

Once upon a time, in the great Thar desert of Rajasthan, there lived a man with seventeen camels. When he was seventy-five years old, he decided to give away his wealth to his three sons and live the last few years of his life on his own, searching for peace. He was not fond of tearful farewells, so he wrote a will and left quietly one night.

Early the next morning when the sun was painting a small pink streak across the sky, the sons awoke. They were sad to see that their father was gone, but they were also very practical young men. So after a few hours, the eldest son decided it was time to read their father's will.

"To my three sons I leave my seventeen camels," read the will. "One-ninth of these shall go to my youngest, my second son shall have one-third and the eldest shall take half."

The three sons read the will over and over again, but they couldn't agree on what their father wanted them to do.

"Seventeen divided by nine is not quite two, but more than one," said the youngest son. "Since I am to have the smallest portion, it is only fair to give me more than my share. Let me take two."

"No," argued the eldest. "If you take more than your fair share, I will surely get less than mine. I am the eldest, so if anyone is to get a little extra, it ought to be me. Half of seventeen is eight and a half. Since half a camel is of no use to anyone, I should just take nine."

"No," said the middle son. "Why should you take more than your share? A third of seventeen is five and two-thirds. I refuse to take fewer than five and two-thirds, because that is my rightful share."

So they argued and argued until the sun rose high in the sky and the sands shimmered like liquid gold.

At last the youngest son said, "Look, this is clearly too tricky to sort out on our own. Shall we ask someone else for help?"

"You are right. Perhaps we should ask the old woman who lives by the oasis," suggested the eldest.

"A good idea," the middle son agreed.

The youngest nodded. "They say she is very wise woman," he said.

So the brothers roped the camels together. The eldest climbed on the back of the first camel, the middle son climbed onto the second camel, and the youngest son climbed onto the back of the very last camel. They rode together to the small pool of water, near which they saw the old woman sitting in the shade of her hut. The three brothers dismounted and greeted her respectfully.

She glanced at them standing before her with bowed heads. "Is something the matter, my sons?" she asked.

"Grandmother, we need your help," said the eldest son. "Our father left us seventeen camels. I am to inherit half of these, but half of seventeen is neither nine nor eight. I think I should take nine but my brothers don't agree."

"Why not?" asked the old woman, raising her eyebrows.

"If he takes more than his share, I will get less, and I'm not willing to give up my fair share," explained the second son.

"What is your fair share?" asked the old woman.

"One-third, grandmother. A third of seventeen is not quite six, but more than five. What am I to do? Less than a whole camel is of no use to anyone," said the second son.

Before the woman could say anything, the youngest jumped in with his plea. "I was left only a ninth of the seventeen camels. May I take more than my share, since I am to have the smallest number of camels?"

The brothers began to quarrel again, just as they had all morning. The old woman watched them thoughtfully for a while. Then, laying a hand on the eldest son's shoulder, she said, "You are brothers. Don't fight with one another."

"But then, are we to break the rules that our father set about how to divide his wealth?" said the eldest son. "Is that what we must do?"

The wise woman closed her eyes. "You have a difficult problem. Seventeen is a hard number to divide," she said.

"What are we to do?" asked the youngest son, his forehead furrowed with worry.

"Do you see that camel in my yard?" the old woman said. "Bring him here and tie him alongside the other camels. We will add him to your wealth."

"We can't do that! We can't take your camel!" gasped the eldest in surprise. The other two stared at her, too touched by her generosity to utter a word.

"Do as I say," she commanded.

The sons obeyed. When all eighteen camels were tied together, the wise woman spoke to the youngest son. "Was not your share a ninth?"

"Yes, grandmother," he said meekly.

"Can you divide eighteen by nine?"

"Yes, that would be two."

"Good. That is correct," the old woman said approvingly. "Now, would you be happy with two camels?"

"Yes, for it is more than my share," said the youngest happily.

"Choose two of your father's camels and promise to argue no more," she said.

"I promise!" the youngest son said hastily, trying to hide the joy in his voice. He chose the two strongest and best, and hurried away.

The other two brothers were quite upset. Now, surely, they would get less!

The wise woman beckoned to the second son. "Was your share a third?"

"Yes," he said in a disgruntled tone. "I should get no less than five and two-thirds."

"Eighteen divided by three is six. Take any six, other than mine, and swear that you will remain content."

"Of course I will! That is more, not less, than five and two-thirds," the middle son exclaimed joyfully. He chose six fine camels and sped rapidly away because he was sure that the woman had made a grave error.

The eldest brother was extremely upset. "Grandmother, I deserve at least eight and a half camels," he said, unable to hide his disappointment. "Why did you give my brothers more and leave less for me?"

"Patience, my son. You will get half of eighteen instead of seventeen. Do you know what that is?"

"Yes, it is nine," the eldest son replied with righteous indignation.

"Then take the nine that are not mine," said the wise woman.

The brother stared in front of him, and was surprised to see that there were, indeed, nine camels other than the woman's.

"You have worked a miracle!" he gasped.

"Not quite," the woman said modestly.

"How can we ever thank you?" he asked, still overwhelmed.

"By living in peace with your brothers," she replied.

And as the eldest son walked away with his nine fine camels, she rose from beneath the palm tree and walked over to her own camel.

"You made the difference, old friend," she said, stroking his warm neck. The camel nuzzled her elbow. Together they watched the last shred of red sky disappear into the darkness of the desert dusk.

Playing with figures ...

Some numbers, like 18, are easy to divide because they have many factors. A factor of a number is an exact divisor of that number. 1, 2, 3, 6, 9 and 18 are factors of 18, and can divide it completely, without leaving any remainder. For example, $18 \div 3 = 6$, $18 \div 2 = 9$, and $18 \div 9 = 2$. Or, written another way, half of eighteen is nine ($\frac{1}{2} \times 18 = 9$); a third of eighteen is six ($\frac{1}{3} \times 18 = 6$); and a ninth of eighteen is two ($\frac{1}{9} \times 18 = 2$).

But not all numbers have as many factors. 17, in fact, has just two factors: 1 and 17. $17 \div 1 = 17$ and $17 \div 17 = 1$. $17 \div 2$ will leave a remainder; so will $17 \div 3$ and $17 \div 9$.

17 and all other numbers like 17 that have only two factors (1 and the number itself) are known as prime numbers. And the number 1 is very special because it is the only number that has just one factor — itself.

How does all this relate to the story?

The father's will left the brothers confused because all the shares ended up with fractions — awkward, because how does one divide a camel without taking its life?

If the brothers had known how to 'round off' the answers to their divisions, they could have solved the problem themselves. Rounding off is done when the result of a calculation contains a fractional part. When the fractional part is half or more than half, it is rounded up to the next (higher) whole number. If the fraction is less than half, it is approximated to the closest lower whole number.

For example, the youngest son had to divide 17 by 9, which is $1\,{}^{8}/_{9}$. Since eight-ninths is more than a half, $1\,{}^{8}/_{9}$ can be rounded to 2, which is the next whole number after 1.

The middle son's share was $5\,{}^{2}/_{3}$. Again, two-thirds is more than half, so $5\,{}^{2}/_{3}$ rounds off to the next highest whole number, which is 6.

The eldest had $8\,{}^{1}/_{2}$. Since half or any fraction over half is rounded to the next highest number, $8\,{}^{1}/_{2}$ rounds to 9.

The woman didn't bother explaining the mathematics to the brothers. She simply did some smart calculations in her head: ${}^{18}/_{9} = 2$, ${}^{18}/_{3} = 6$, ${}^{18}/_{2} = 9$ and $2+6+9 = 17$, and realised that if she pretended to give the brothers her camel they could divide 18 instead of the prime number 17, and get satisfying whole numbers — or camels — as results and, of course, in the end she would get her own camel back.

Filling a Space

An Ethiopian folktale

There once lived a wise and wealthy farmer. When he grew so old that he could see the shadow of death, he decided to divide his property among his sons. His eldest son was called Girma, meaning respectable, or aura of respect; his second son was called Demeke, which means getting brighter, or to brighten up; his youngest son was called Brehanu, which means light.

"Once I die," the farmer thought, "my sons might quarrel. It is best that they know my wishes now and agree to them."

So he called his sons and said, "My children, I want to divide my property amongst you today, while I am still alive. If you wish to question my judgement, you may do so now and I will explain my reasons to you."

"Thank you, Father," said Girma, Demeke and Brehanu.

"My land is easy to divide," said the father. "So each of you will have a portion that is the same size."

"Thank you, Father," the three sons said again.

"Who will inherit the house, father?" Brehanu then asked,

The father smiled and his eyes twinkled. "That is a difficult question. I would like the house to go to the cleverest of my children. Which of you is the cleverest?"

"That is for you to decide, Father," said Girma.

"Indeed it is," the father agreed. "Here is how I will decide." He beckoned to the sons and they went up close to him. He opened his fist. On his palm lay three small coins.

"Here is a coin for each of you," the father said. "Take it to the market and spend it. The one who buys something that can fill this room, will inherit this house. Go now. Remember, you may each spend just this one coin and return before dark."

The house was strongly built and beautiful and all the sons loved it. Each wanted to be the one to whom the house was bequeathed. They left at once for the market. When they reached there they parted ways.

Girma thought for a long time. Then he had an idea. He ran back to the farm, and pushed a wagon to the market. He filled the wagon with straw. There was a lot of straw to be had, even for just one coin. He was very pleased with himself. Perhaps he didn't have enough straw to fill the whole room, but he was sure his purchase would fill more space than anything his brothers could buy.

Demeke thought for a little longer than Girma had done. What could he get with a coin that would be plentiful enough to occupy a lot of space in the room?

Feathers! He could get sacks and sacks of feathers!

"I am sure to get the house!" he shouted joyfully, and he sang all the way back to the farm, carrying the large, light sacks.

Girma and Demeke waited for Brehanu to join them, but the hours went by and he did not appear. Then, just as the sun fell below the horizon and the darkness of twilight began to creep across the ground, Brehanu returned.

Girma smiled when he noticed that Brehanu had neither sack nor wagon. "He has not been able to think of an idea," he thought. "Poor Brehanu!"

"Are you empty-handed, brother?" Demeke burst out in surprise. "Have you already given up?"

Brehanu shook his head. "Not quite," he said.

The sons entered the house together and stood in front of their father, who smiled at them.

"Shall you try first, my firstborn?" he asked Girma.

Girma nodded. He brought the wagon close to the front door and began to spread his straw on the floor. When all the straw had been strewn, the room was still more than half empty.

"Well done," said the father, and Girma smiled.

"Well done, indeed, brother, but perhaps I can do better," said Demeke.

"Perhaps," said the father. "Let us see you try now."

The boys cleared the house of straw, and Demeke began to pour the feathers out of his sacks. When Demeke had emptied the last sack, the room was still less than half full.

The father sneezed slightly because a feather had flown into his nose. "Now we shall see what our youngest has to offer," he said.

The three swept the house clean of feathers, and then Brehanu came into the room, empty-handed. He took something long and thin out of his right pocket. It was a candle, which he placed in the centre of the room. Then he pulled something small out of his left pocket. He struck his match and lit the candle. The flame sputtered and then sparkled into life. It shone steadily, filling the darkening room with a soft light.

"What a clever idea!" Demeke exclaimed.

Girma nodded. Though he was disappointed, he still managed to smile at his youngest brother.

"I think we all agree," said the father, "that the house will go to Brehanu."

Brehanu smiled, his dark eyes dancing in the flickering candlelight.

"Thank you, Father. Thank you, brothers," he said.

Together, Girma, Demeke, and Brehanu lit candles in every room. When the whole house was filled with light, they sat down with their father to share their evening meal.

Does light really fill a space the way straw or feathers do? Not really. But in the story, the father and brothers were obviously charmed by Brehanu's solution to the problem of filling up the space in the room.

Every three-dimensional object occupies space and the amount of space an object occupies is known as its volume. Another way to think of it is that volume is the amount of 'stuff' in the object. The space an object occupies has a lot to do with how long, wide, and tall it is.

How much space is there inside a room? A room is like a three-dimensional rectangle, cuboidal in shape. The volume of a cuboid, is its length multiplied by its width, multiplied by its height. If we pretend that the room the brothers tried to fill in the story was 10 metres high, 6 metres long, and 2 metres wide, its internal volume would be 120 cubic metres: $10m \times 6m \times 2m = 120m^3$.

What is the volume of this book that you're reading? Can you calculate that yourself? The book is cuboidal in shape, of course, so all you need to do is get a ruler and measure the length of its sides, as well as its thickness. Make sure, though, that you measure everything in the same unit — centimetres (cm), or millimetres (mm), or inches. For example, the book might be 5 cm thick, 8 cm wide and 10 cm long. If so, you could multiply all the measurements in centimetres, and express the answer in cubic centimetres ($5cm \times 8cm \times 10cm = 400cm^3$). Or, you could express everything in millimeters ($50mm \times 80mm \times 100mm = 40,000mm^3$). Whatever you do, don't try to multiply or divide or add or subtract

something which you measured in centimetres with something you measured in millimetres.

Of course, the volume of some objects, such as cuboids, is easier to measure than the volume of some others. But even in ancient times, people found ways to calculate the volumes of shapes that were far more complex than the cuboid.

The ancient Egyptians had to calculate the volume of any pyramid they wanted to build. Otherwise, they wouldn't have been able to plan for how much material they needed for its construction, among other things. They discovered that the volume of a pyramid with a square base = $\frac{1}{3}$ × area of the pyramid's base × pyramid's height. The Egyptians realised how important it was to preserve their mathematical knowledge, so they wrote down important problems and solutions on papyrus. In 1848, a British collector named Rhind acquired a papyrus containing a collection of 112 problems with solutions. This was originally named the Rhind papyrus but modern historians call it the Ahmes papyrus because it was written by an Egyptian scribe called Ahmes.

Other ancient cultures also came up with 'identities' that helped to calculate the volumes of three-dimensional objects. In China, a book called the *Chiu Chang* was used as a reference text by engineers and architects. It has rules for computing the volumes of three-dimensional shapes used in the construction of castles, houses and canals.

An Indian mathematician called Brahmagupta, who lived around

598 – 660 CE, devised 'identities' for the volumes of many solids.
Aryabhata, an Indian mathematician and astronomer who preceded
Brahmagupta and lived around 475 – 550 CE, compiled the mathematics
of his time in a book called the *Aryabhatiya*. This was translated into Latin
in the thirteenth century and it was through this that European
mathematicians eventually learned the method for calculating the volumes
of spheres.

The Weight of a Crown

a legend from Greece

Many, many years ago, King Hiero of Syracuse in ancient Greece decided to get a new gold crown made for himself. He gave the order to a jeweller whom he trusted. But this jeweller was very old, and died before the crown was delivered to the king.

Now the king was worried. What if the crown hadn't been finished by the trusted jeweller after all? What if one of his assistants had finished it, and stolen some of the gold? Was there any way to tell how much gold had gone into making the crown? Was it possible to find out if the crown was of pure gold, without destroying it?

The king had no idea what to do, and so he sent for Archimedes, the scientist-mathematician who helped him out now and then. Archimedes listened gravely to the king. As he walked away from the palace towards home, his head was bent in thought. This was a tough problem.

All night long he worried about it, without coming up with a solution. Indeed, he spent the whole week doing nothing but thinking.

He realised that if the density of the material in the crown was the same as the density of gold, it would prove that the crown was indeed made of gold. Density was mass divided by volume. Archimedes could measure the mass of the crown by weighing it in a balance. But how on earth could he find out the volume of the crown?

The volume of a cube was easy to measure — it was length times breadth times height. But how was he to accurately measure the volume of an object as oddly shaped as the king's crown?

By the end of the week, his wife had had enough.

"Archimedes, you may have a difficult problem on your hands, but you stink!" she said to him. "Go bathe!"

"Alright, alright," Archimedes agreed reluctantly.

He filled the bathtub with water and, still deep in thought, placed his foot into it. Water rose slightly in the tub. He sank his whole leg into it, watching the water rise higher. Then he plunged himself into the tub and some of the water sloshed out.

"Eureka!" he yelled suddenly. "Eureka! I have found it!"

He leaped out of the tub and ran out of the bathroom, shouting joyously. Yes! He had found the solution to the problem!

He ran out of the house, shouting "Eureka! Eureka!" at the top of his voice.

When he returned his wife was waiting.

"Archimedes," she said, shaking her head. "Do you know what you just did? You ran all about town without any clothes on."

Archimedes looked startled for a second. Then he smiled.

"Who cares!" he said. "I'll be remembered for solving the king's problem."

"That, and running around the city naked!" said his wife.

She was right. Centuries later, Archimedes is remembered for both.

a mathematical idea ...

Archimedes realised that to find out if the crown was pure gold or not, he needed to determine the density of the metal making up the crown. If the crown was made of pure gold, its density would be equal to the density of pure gold.

Density = Mass ÷ Volume.

Archimedes could determine the mass of the crown by weighing it. But how could he find out the volume of the crown?

When stepping into the bath, Archimedes was struck by an idea — that the water displaced in the tub was equal to the volume of the part of his body submerged underwater. The next day, he weighed the crown using a balance. Then he measured its volume — by immersing it in water filled to the brim of a container, and measuring the volume of water that it displaced. Once he knew the weight and volume of the crown, he divided weight by volume, to get an idea of the density of the crown.

The story goes that the density of the crown determined by Archimedes was not the same as the density of gold. Apparently, the goldsmith had not used pure gold to make the king's crown.

Among the ancient European cultures, the Greeks were probably the most advanced in science, mathematics and technology, and were often the first to make major discoveries in many areas of knowledge. Solving the king's problem gave Archimedes another idea. This idea became known as 'the Archimedes principle'. It explains why some objects float and others sink.

The Archimedes principle states that a body partially or wholly submerged in a fluid experiences an upward thrust equal to the weight of the fluid that it displaces. If the object floats, then the weight of the water it displaces is equal to the weight of the object. This is why really heavy boats are very large — if the part of the boat in the water was small, only a small volume of water would be displaced, and if the weight of the displaced water was less than the weight of the boat, the boat would sink.

How Many Stars?

A folktale from India

As Gopal was bouncing stones across the village pond one day, he saw the reflection of a well-dressed man wearing a jewelled turban, walking by the water, head bent deep in thought.

"Oh! Who are you?" Gopal asked him. "Where are you from? What brings you here? Why are you so troubled?"

"So many questions from so small a person!" said the man, turning to Gopal.

Gopal looked up at him, unabashed. "Perhaps I can help you," he offered.

The man sighed and sat on a stone. He took off his turban and shook his head slowly.

"No one can help," he said. "We are all lost."

"Lost? I'm not lost. I know who I am and where I am!" said Gopal.

The man smiled sadly.

"It is only for a short while longer that you will know where you are," he said. "Soon you will be elsewhere, though you will still be in this village. Soon you will be someone else, though you will not have changed."

"What do you mean?" asked Gopal.

"This village is about to become part of another kingdom," said the man. "You will no longer be a free person; you will become one of the many oppressed,

conquered subjects of the clever Nawab whose land borders our kingdom."

Gopal was surprised. "How?" he asked. "There has been no war."

"Yes, that is the only thing that we can be thankful for," said the man. "At least the Nawab's takeover will not cause bloodshed."

"How can the Nawab take us over?" asked Gopal.

"He invited our King to his palace," the man replied. "While he was there, the Nawab tricked the King into promising to hand over his kingdom in a week, unless he could answer a particular question. The Nawab's question is not one that is answerable and so our King, who is an honest man of his word, will have to hand over the kingdom tomorrow."

"What is this question?" asked Gopal. "Perhaps I can answer it."

"You?" said the man with an amused smile. "All of us, the King's entire council of ministers, tried to come up with the answer and we could not. No one can. The Nawab asked us how many stars there were in the sky. Even if we tried to count them all night, every night, we would not be done in a week — not even in a lifetime."

"How many stars are there in the sky?" Gopal repeated.

He thought for a moment and then, his eyes twinkling like stars, he said brightly, "That's an easy question. I know the answer to that."

"This is serious," the man said.

"Of course," replied Gopal.

The man looked hard at him. He could tell that the boy was sincere.

"Take me to the palace at once," urged Gopal. We must reach the king tonight, before he meets the Nawab tomorrow."

"What is the answer?" asked the man.

"It is for the ears of the King and then for the ears of the Nawab," said Gopal.

The man could tell that Gopal was stubborn.

"Well, let us be off then," he said. He whistled and a lovely black stallion came galloping down to where he sat. He leaped up onto the stallion's back and

Gopal jumped on after him. They rode at a furious pace, and reached the palace by nightfall. The man took Gopal into the King's chambers and left him there.

The next morning, the man noticed that the King was smiling.

"You have found a treasure," the King said. "That boy is a gem."

The King rode to meet the Nawab, Gopal following him in a palanquin.

The Nawab was waiting. "Have you come to hand over your kingdom?" he asked pleasantly.

"No," said the King. "I have come to answer your question."

The Nawab glared. "No one can answer that question," he said.

"Oh yes, someone can," said Gopal, leaping out of the palanquin.

"How many stars are there in the sky?" thundered the Nawab, trying to look as intimidating as he could.

"As many as there are grains of sand on all the beaches in the world," answered Gopal.

The Nawab's jaw fell open. It was a good while before he remembered to close it again. He coughed and cleared his throat.

"Since we have answered your question, you must promise to leave us in peace forever," said Gopal severely. "It's not a good thing to try and take over your neighbour's land."

The Nawab looked helpless. "I was only joking, you know," he said. "Only joking."

"Sure," said the King. "So let's sign a peace treaty here and now."

When the king returned to his kingdom, brandishing the peace treaty victoriously, his ministers shouted with joy. One of them was the happiest of all — the one who had found Gopal.

"Will you not stay and work with us, wise one?" he asked.

Gopal smiled. "I will," he said.

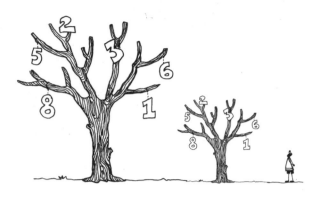

big, bigger...

Is the number of stars in the sky really the same as the number of grains of sand on the earth? Who knows? Probably not.

Gopal was only trying to prove a point and so he came up with a huge number that was impossible for him or anyone else of his time to accurately count. Nowadays, scientists and mathematicians often use huge numbers. Astronomers, who study starry skies, also need to deal with large numbers. So do geologists, who study sands and beaches.

Big numbers are fun to think of, though difficult to write. Sometimes we express them in terms of powers, which are just numbers multiplied by themselves. For example, instead of writing 1,000,000,000, you could just as well write 10^9 (because if you multiplied ten by itself nine times, you'd end up with that gigantic number).

Scientists use special units to describe large quantities. For instance, in metric units, 'mega-' means something multiplied by 1,000,000. Or, thinking mathematically, 'mega-' means (× 1,000,000). Equally well, you could say that 'mega-' is a word to help think of 10^6. So a megawatt is 10^6 watts. What about 1,000,000,000? Scientists have a special word for numbers in that range, too: 'giga-'. So, 'giga-' means (×1,000,000,000). Equally well, you could say that 'giga-' is a word to help think of 10^9. A gigawatt is 10^9 watts. A 'googol' is 10^{100} — a very, very large number, after which the search engine Google is named!

Gourmet Roulette

A Russian braintwister

One cold winter afternoon, ten professors went to a restaurant for a meal. It was the first time they had ventured out of their university to eat together, and as they approached the rectangular table they were uncertain about how they should sit. Each of them wanted to be at the head of the table.

"It seems to me," said the learned language professor, "that we should sit in alphabetical order. Since my name starts with the first letter of the alphabet, I will sit at the head of the table."

The oldest professor was visibly upset by this idea.

"I am the eldest," said he, "so it is my right to sit at the head of the table."

"On the contrary," said the youngest, "I am the newest and most creative one of all. I should sit at the head of the table."

"I think," said the geography professor, "that we should sit geographically. Among all of us here, I come from the northernmost city in Russia, and I should therefore sit at the head of the table, which we will take to be north. The rest of you can seat yourselves southwards, according to the location of your hometowns."

This went on. Each professor weighed in with an opinion and their voices grew louder and louder. The proprietor of the restaurant was concerned that this silly argument would disturb the peace and drive away other customers. Then again, he didn't want the professors to leave either.

A young waiter noticed the worried frown on the proprietor's face and said, "Don't worry. I have an idea."

He approached the grumbling group with a lively greeting. "Hullo, hullo! May I interrupt?"

The professors quietened down and turned around to see who had cut into their discussion.

"Why don't you stop arguing and sit down where I tell you to today," the waiter suggested. "I'll write down the order in which you are sitting. The next time you return — tomorrow, or next week perhaps — sit in a different order. Do this until you've sat in every possible way, and on the day when you've completely run through these ways and have to sit again the way that you are sitting today, we will give you a free meal."

The professors smiled at the young waiter. One of them clapped him on his back.

"What an excellent suggestion!" he said. "Yes, let's do as he says and soon we'll get a free meal."

Eager to make this good deal, the others sat down to eat.

The waiter returned to the proprietor, who was still looking somewhat worried.

"Well, young man, you've solved the problem for today, but I'm not looking forward to giving away ten free meals," the proprietor said.

The waiter smiled.

"When I'm not waiting at tables, I study mathematics at the University," he said. "Don't worry, you'll never have to give away a free meal. Not for another 10,000 years or so, even if they returned every day."

"Are you certain?" asked the proprietor, puzzled.

"Absolutely," said the waiter. "You see, there are 3,628,800 ways in which ten people can sit around a table."

"How do you know?"

"I'll show you," said the waiter. He picked up a knife and a fork. "In how many ways can we arrange these two objects?" he asked.

"Easy. Two ways. Knife on the left, fork on the right, or fork on the left, knife on the right."

"Precisely." The waiter picked up a spoon. "Now there are three objects. How many ways are possible with three different objects?"

The proprietor had to think. He placed the spoon on the left, the knife in the middle, and the fork on the right. Then, leaving the spoon where it was, he switched the positions of the fork and knife. Those were two possibilities. How many more arrangements could he think of? He proceeded systematically.

"There are six ways to arrange three objects," he said after some more experimentation.

"Good," said the waiter. "Now, let's add a plate into the mix. If you have four objects, can you calculate how many possible ways there could be?"

The proprietor arranged the objects in different ways, and recorded the different arrangements in order not to repeat them. It was fun, but he could see that it would quickly get tedious.

"There are twenty-four ways to arrange four objects," he said. "But don't give me another and tell me to work it out. It would take too much time. Is there some general mathematical rule that you know and I don't?"

The young waiter nodded, smiling from ear to ear.

"Can you guess?" he asked.

"Two objects, two ways. Three objects, six ways. Four objects, twenty four ways." He was lost in deep thought for while, but finally gave up.

"This is the rule," said the waiter. "Two different objects can be arranged in $2 \times 1 = 2$ different ways without repetition. For three objects, there are $3 \times 2 \times 1 = 6$ different ways possible. With four objects, the number of ways is $4 \times 3 \times 2 \times 1 = 24$."

"Aha!" said the proprietor catching on. "So for five objects the number of possible ways would be 5×4×3×2×1, is that correct?"

"Yes."

"Fascinating! So the number of ways in which these ten professors can sit around the table is 10×9×8×7×6×5×4×3×2×1, whatever that is."

"That number," said the waiter triumphantly, "is 3,628,800."

The proprietor grinned.

"You've earned yourself a raise, young man," he said. "One of these days, you'll take my place."

"Thanks for the raise," replied the waiter. "One of these days, I hope to be a professor at the University myself."

"By that time," said the proprietor to the young prodigy, "I sincerely hope you have more congenial and less conceited colleagues than the ones we have at our restaurant today."

The waiter chuckled.

"I hope so too," he said, glancing in the direction of the ten professors who had finally stopped arguing and were sitting patiently, waiting for their meal. "It's a good thing my mathematics professor wasn't with them, or I would never have been able to pull off this trick."

Do you know that the exclamation mark has a mathematical meaning? It even has a different name. In maths, the symbol '!' is called a factorial.

The factorial is a convenient way to write a special type of mathematical sentence. Instead of writing $10\times9\times8\times7\times6\times5\times4\times3\times2\times1$, we can simply say 10!. So, if we write 5!, it means $1\times2\times3\times4\times5$, or $5\times4\times3\times2\times1$, whichever way you prefer (ascending order from one to the number, or in descending order from the number to one).

Following that same logic, $4! = 4\times3\times2\times1 = 24$, and $3! = 3\times2\times1 = 6$, and $2! = 2\times1 = 2$. So can you think what 1! means?

$1! = 1$. That is to say, one factorial is equal to one.

We can make a generalisation and say that for any number n, n! is the product of the consecutive numbers 1 through n (if you like counting up). Of course, if you prefer to count down, you could say n! is the product of the consecutive numbers n through 1, and that would be true, too, because as we said earlier, the order doesn't matter. Order doesn't matter when you multiply numbers, or add them. You can go backwards or forwards with n!, as you like.

So, if your bookshelf has just three books including this one, how many ways could you arrange these books? Pretend that the three books are called Math Folktales, Maths Textbook, and Maths Storybook.

Here's the long way to do this problem. You can arrange the three books in these ways:

1. Math Folktales, Maths Textbook, and Maths Storybook
2. Math Folktales, Maths Storybook and Maths Textbook.
3. Maths Textbook, Math Folktales, and Maths Story book
4. Maths Textbook, Maths Storybook, and Math Folktales.
5. Maths Storybook, Math Folktales and Maths Textbook.
6. Maths Storybook, Maths Textbook, and Math Folktales.

The short way to solve this problem is to use the Russian waiter's technique: the number of ways to arrange all 3 objects (without repetition, and without leaving out any of the books, of course) is 3!. You know this rule, so instead of taking the time to actually arrange the books and see experimentally how many ways are possible, you can quickly say that there are 6 ways to arrange 3 books on your shelf, because $3! = 3 \times 2 \times 1 = 6$.

A Fair Division

An Indian story

In a little village in India, there lived two farmers, good friends, called Raju and Shyam. Every day they set out to work together, each carrying a bundle in which their wives packed lunch. Usually it was a simple meal of rice and dal. But sometimes the wives would squeeze in the time to make hot, stuffed parathas.

Every day around noon, Raju and Shyam took a short break from work and sat together to share their lunch. After hours of working under a hot sun that had blazed down on their bare backs, they came together one day to sit cross-legged in the shade of a great banyan tree. They untied their cloth bundles to see what they had for lunch.

"Ah, parathas!" exclaimed Raju. "Dripping with ghee!"

Shyam looked to see what he had with him.

"I too have parathas!" he cried.

Though the parathas had been made by two different women, there was no telling them apart. They looked the same and were nearly exactly the same size, but Raju had three parathas and Shyam had five.

To share as usual, they placed all their parathas together in one big stack and were about to cut the stack in two and eat half each, when a young traveller greeted them politely. He looked weary.

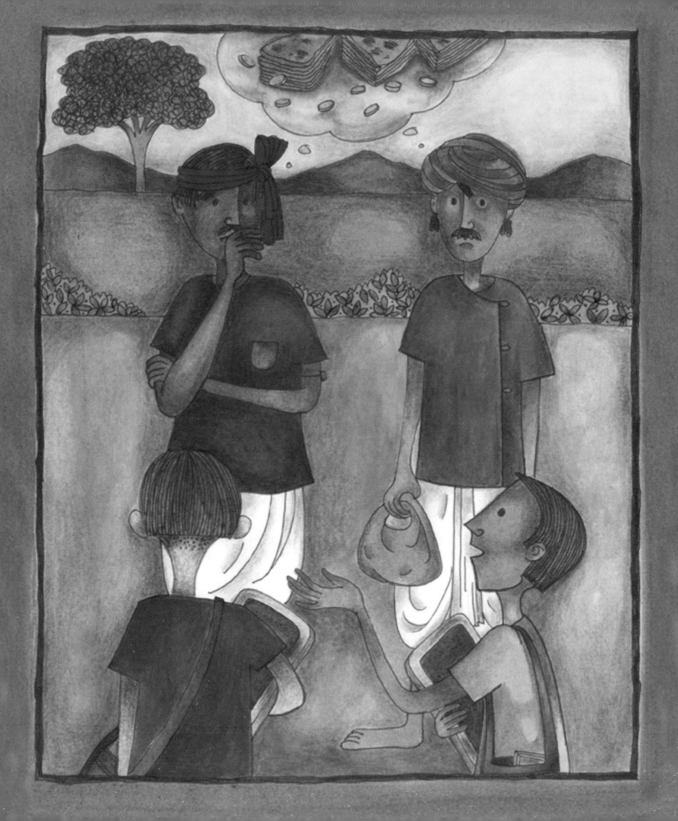

The farmers looked at one another and the same thought went through their minds. "Would you like to share our meal?" they asked.

"You are so kind," the young traveller said gratefully. "That would be wonderful. Those parathas are making my mouth water."

So Raju and Shyam divided their stack into three equal parts, and they all ate together, sharing equally and relishing their simple meal. When they had finished, the traveller thanked them profusely. He then reached into a silken pouch that hung by his waist and fished out eight shiny gold coins.

The farmers gasped in surprise. They had never seen so much gold before.

"No, no," Raju said, shaking his head. "You don't owe us any money."

"We gave you our food gladly," said Shyam. "Not for payment."

"I too am giving this willingly. I am happy to have met you," said the traveller.

Though the farmers still shook their heads, the traveller insisted, thanked them again, and left the eight gold coins where the parathas had been before continuing on his way.

The farmers stared at the gold.

"We can't leave this money here," said Shyam.

"He leaves us no choice but to take it," Raju agreed.

"But how shall we divide it?" asked Raju. "There are eight coins and two of us. It seems to me that we should take four coins each. That would be a fair division, would it not?"

Shyam scratched his head. "Hmmmm . . .," he said slowly. "I brought five parathas today, and you brought just three. So it seems to me as though we didn't quite start off equally, don't you think?"

Raju looked thoughtful. "What are you suggesting?" he asked.

"I am thinking," Shyam went on, "that I should take five coins and you should keep three. That seems fair to me."

Raju did not want to quarrel with his friend, but he was not convinced by Shyam's argument.

Just then, they saw their sons returning from the village school. The two boys waved and came up to them.

"What is the matter?" asked Raju's son, looking into his father's troubled face.

"Well, well, nothing for you to worry about," said Raju.

"In fact, it almost looks like the two of you are fighting," said Shyam's son. Shyam did not know what to say. So he told them the truth.

"A traveller paid us for some food that we gave him," he said, "but we aren't sure how to divide the money."

"I can tell you. We learn division at school," said Shyam's son, confidently.

"It's much too complicated for you," said Raju. You see, I had three parathas and Shyam had five parathas. We stacked them up and divided the pile into three parts. Each of us ate equally. Then the traveller gave us eight gold coins. How do we divide these properly between the two of us?"

"Easy," said his son, after thinking quickly. "You get one coin and Shyam Chacha gets seven."

"What!" exclaimed Raju, shocked. "That's rubbish."

"I'd love to take seven coins," said Shyam, "but that seems just wrong to me."

His son looked at him scornfully. "You are both worse at mathematics than anyone we know," he said. "You deserve seven, and Raju Chacha one."

"Why do I deserve seven?" asked Shyam, suspiciously.

The boys laughed. "Think!" they said and ran away to play.

The two men sat together and thought about it for a long time. Finally Raju said, "Shyam, we have been friends for many years. Sometimes you have more parathas, and sometimes I have more. This is the first and only time we've been paid for them. I don't want to fight over this. Our friendship is too precious. I'll agree to whatever you decide."

Shyam smiled at his friend. "You are right," he said. "I don't think I deserve seven coins. I don't even understand this division. Let us just take four each and stay friends."

Raju smiled. Later that evening he told his wife the story.

"You were lucky," she said. "You should only have been given one coin."

"That's what our son said," said Raju. "But why?"

"How many parathas were there altogether?" asked his wife

"My three and Shyam's five," said Raju. "Eight parathas in total."

"How many of you shared the parathas?"

"Three."

"Good. Since you stacked up the parathas and cut it in equal thirds, how many parts were there after that?"

"Er . . .," Raju began.

"Eight parathas, and each is cut into three parts . . ." his wife prompted.

"Ah . . ." said Raju.

"If each of eight parathas was cut into three pieces, there were twenty-four pieces before you started eating," his wife said.

"Yes, twenty-four," said Raju quickly. "I knew that. After we cut up the stack, there were twenty-four equal paratha parts to share equally amongst us."

"So how many parts did each of you eat?" asked his wife.

"Hmmm . . ." said Raju.

"Twenty-four parts, divided equally among three men, how many for each?" prompted his wife.

"Twenty-four divided by three, did you say?" asked Raju.

"Yes," said his wife patiently. "Each of you ate eight parts, is that correct?"

"Of course. Each of us ate eight parts," Raju repeated. "So the man paid one coin for each part!"

"Remember how many full parathas Shyam had to start with?"

"Five," said Raju, relieved with the easy question.

"So, of the twenty-four pieces, how many came from Shyam's parathas?"

"Now, that," said Raju, "is just the question I was asking myself."

Raju's wife shook her head and smiled indulgently. "Fifteen parts came out of

Shyam's parathas, because each of his five parathas was cut into three pieces, and five threes are fifteen. Let's say that out of these Shyam ate eight and your guest ate seven. The traveller would then owe Shyam seven coins, if each part was worth one coin. You, Raju, had a total of nine parts, since three threes are nine. You ate eight of these parts yourself, leaving only one for your guest. So you should have just one gold coin."

"Ha," said Raju. "But what if the traveller ate four parts from my parathas and four from Shyam's? Or five from mine and three from his?"

His wife sighed. "In every case, the answer would be the same," she said. "Because then it would mean you would have eaten some of Shyam's parts and would owe him coins for what you ate of his parathas."

Their son ran in. "I'm hungry!" he announced.

And they sat down to another meal.

figuring it right ...

Do you agree with Raju's wife and son? How many coins do you think Raju deserved — four, three, or just one?

If you are having trouble finding the right answer, try to go step by step, and work out the way Raju's wife was thinking. The easiest way to think of the problem is the way she did: out of the 8 parts that the traveller ate, only 1 came from Raju's parathas, while the other 7 came from Shyam's.

If you are the type who likes to think of alternative possibilities — which is a very good way to think — you might ask, what if the traveller ate 4 parts from Raju's and 4 parts from Shyam's parathas? Or 5 from Shyam's and 3 from Raju's?

In all these cases, you'll find the answer is the same. That's because each man ate an equal share of food. So in these other cases, Raju would have had to eat a few parts from Shyam's parathas. Raju would owe Shyam a coin for each piece he ate that was not his own. After paying Shyam back, he'd find himself with just one coin.

But then again, all this is fair only if we disregard the issue of friendship. Good friendships can be broken by quarrels over money — but sometimes, as in the case of Raju and Shyam, they are strong enough to not divide over a matter of division. Can one really put a price on sharing?

Criss-cross Logic

A 'thinking' American folktale

Once, after a long journey, a farmer had to cross a fast-moving river to get home. He had with him a dog, a rooster and a sack of corn. Neither the farmer, nor the dog, or the rooster, could swim.

The farmer hired a boat, but it was not big enough for him to take everything across at once. The boat was in fact so small that, at any one time, it could take only one of his possessions in addition to himself.

The farmer had to be in the boat every time he made a trip, of course, as he was the only one who could ferry the boat across. But he faced a dilemma.

He did not want to make the dog stay alone on the bank with the rooster, because the dog was a hungry hunting hound which would undoubtedly devour the rooster.

Likewise, he did not want to leave the rooster alone with the corn, because hungry roosters were not to be trusted and, in his absence, it would quite certainly eat up the corn.

He stood at the bank and thought hard. The river would soon be in spate. He had to get across as soon as he could. For his own safety, it was not wise to risk more trips across the river than were absolutely essential. The waters were wild and rising higher with every moment that he delayed.

What was the fewest number of trips he could make to carry all three of his possessions safely across the river?

Five, he realised. Just five.

How did he do it?

spinning off ...

The German mathematician Leibniz wrote: "Music is a secret arithmetical exercise and the person who indulges in it does not realise that he is manipulating numbers." The Persian poet Omar Khayyam was also an excellent mathematician. Yet, when we speak about creativity we usually think of the arts rather than of the sciences.

This is probably because maths and science are both based on logic and at first glance, creativity seems to have little to do with logic. However, logic can be used in creative ways. The best scientists and mathematicians make creative leaps of imagination to come up with solutions to puzzles that others, who are less creative, have been unable

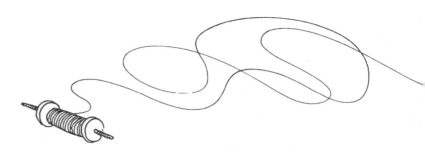

to solve. Often, such scientists and mathematicians are unable to express precisely what it is that helped them arrive at the ingenious solution. The creative process defies description.

This short folktale has many versions and is commonly told in India, parts of Africa, and the Americas. Each time the animals vary — with a leopard or fox, a goat or hen, grass or straw. But the farmer's problem is always the same.

To this there are at least two possible solutions. Here's one:

On the first trip, the farmer leaves the dog alone with the corn and takes the rooster across to the far bank.

He returns with an empty boat, and takes the dog across next.

He drops the dog off and brings the rooster back with him (as he can't leave the dog and rooster together on the far bank).

Then he drops the rooster off and takes the corn to the far bank. He returns again with an empty boat. (The dog and the corn are alone together on the far bank, now, which is just fine.)

For the final trip, he picks up the rooster, takes it to the far bank, and proceeds on his journey.

The second solution? Get creative!

Sixty-Four Rings to Heaven

A number tale from Vietnam

There was a king of Hanoi who was good, kind and just. The people loved him. He had just one flaw — he spent a lot of time worrying about one very unlikely event. He worried about when the world would end.

Slowly, he became more and more obsessed with this worry and began to neglect affairs of the state. He asked every wise person he met the answer to his question. But no one knew, and that only made the king more afraid and worried than ever.

Then one day, a wise man came to visit the king. "Sire," he said, "I have had a dream about the end of the world. In my dream, a spirit came to me and said that you should build a monastery in Hanoi, by the banks of the Red River. Inside the monastery tower, you should place three metal spikes, and on one of the spikes place sixty-four gold rings. The rings should all be of different sizes. The biggest should be at the bottom, and they should get progressively smaller, with the smallest right at the top."

"What does this have to do with how much longer the world will exist?" asked the King, baffled.

"The monks who live in the tower will have to do one job as they meditate," continued the wise man. "They must transpose the rings from one spike to another, using the third spike as an aid. There is a rule about these transpositions that must never be broken. Only one ring must be transposed at a time, and it is forbidden to ever place a bigger ring on top of a smaller one. When all the rings have been transferred, the world will come to an end."

The King built the temple at Hanoi, and told the monks to inform him as they got close to the end of their task. Knowing that his question would soon be answered, and that he would at least be warned before the end of the world approached, the King moved on to other things, and began once again to pay attention to his duties.

The monks did not finish the task as long as the King lived. In fact, though they began their work thousands of years ago, their successors are still doing it. Can you tell how long it will take to complete their job?

winding down ...

Sometimes, the best way to approach a problem is by doing an experiment. Try this practical solution to the puzzle of the Tower of Hanoi.

Get 4 coins of differing sizes. Stack them on a saucer, with the most valuable coin at the bottom, and the rest in decreasing order with the coin of lowest value at the top. Put two more saucers on the table. You have to move all the coins into the third saucer, stacked the same way as they were in the beginning (with the most valuable coin at the bottom, and the rest in decreasing order with the coin of lowest value at the top). You may use the second saucer as a temporary holding place, but you have to follow these rules:

1. You should end up with them in the same order on the third saucer.
2. You may move only one coin at one time. You cannot lift two coins together and swap them or anything else like that.
3. Never place a place a bigger coin on a smaller one.

Here's a hint. If the number of coins is odd, then put the first into the third saucer; if the number of coins is even, start with the second saucer.

What is the least amount of moves you need to accomplish your goal?

Now, repeat the experiment using 3 coins and then just two. Do you notice any pattern? Can you make a general rule based on this pattern?

If you did everything correctly, this is what you'll find:

With just 2 coins, you'd need 3 moves — lower value coin into the middle saucer, higher value coin into third saucer, lower value coin into the third saucer. Say we write it as 2^2-1, which is 4–1, and equals 3.

If you start with 3 coins in the first saucer, you need 7 moves. First move two smaller coins into middle saucer — 3 moves, and then move the largest into the third saucer, then move two coins from middle to third which is another 3 moves. So this may be written as $3+1+3$ or 2^3-1, both of which equal 7.

For 4 coins, move the smaller three into the middle, which is seven moves. Then transpose the biggest one into the third saucer; and then the three smaller coins into the third, which is another 7 moves. Following the earlier pattern, we can write this as $7+1+7$ or 2^4-1, both of which equal 15.

So, even without doing it, you might be able to guess the number of moves with 5 coins. Can you? If you are thinking it will then require $2^5-1 = 32-1 = 31$ moves, you are correct.

That means, because the monks in the story have 64 rings, they will need 2 raised to the power of 64 minus one moves altogether — or, writing mathematically, $2^{64}-1$. So even if each transposition takes only a second, which would be an unrealistically short a time, it means in one hour they can make 3,600 transpositions. Even working at such a fast speed, all night and all day, they would make only about 100,000 moves a day. They would need over 580,000,000,000 years to finish the job!

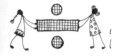

Mathematwist: number tales from around the world

ISBN 978-81-8146-357-9
© *text* T. V. Padma
© *illustrations* Proiti Roy
First published in India, 2007
Reprinted in 2009, 2010

design Radhika Menon

The original version of Rounding Up Camels *appeared in* Odyssey *magazine (part of the* Cricket *magazine group, USA); it is reprinted here with permission from Cobblestone-Carus Publications.*

The original version of A Fair Division *appeared in* Highlights for Children*, USA; it is reprinted here with permission from the Highlights Foundation.*

Published by
Tulika Publishers, 13 Prithvi Avenue First Street, Abhiramapuram, Chennai 600 018, India
email tulikabooks@vsnl.com *website* www.tulikabooks.com

Printed and bound by
Sudarsan Graphics, 27 Neelakanta Mehta Street, T.Nagar, Chennai 600 017, India

For more information about Tulika or to order books visit our website.

www.tulikabooks.com